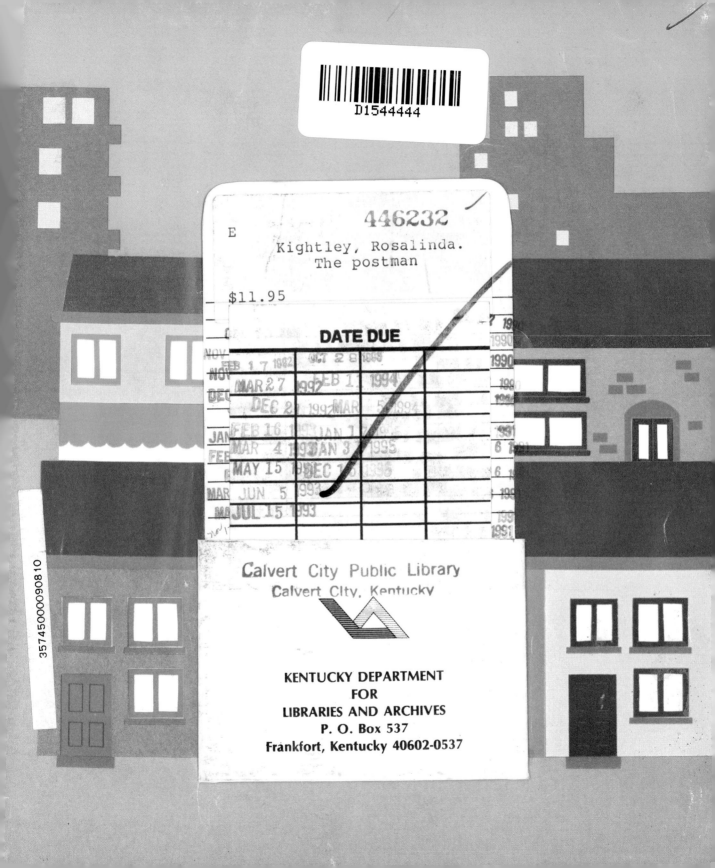

Consultant Gussie Hearsey on behalf of the Pre-school Playgroups Association
©1987 Rosalinda Kightley
Macmillan Publishing Company
866 Third Avenue, New York, NY 10022
First published 1987 in Great Britain by Walker Books Ltd, London
First American Edition 1988
Printed in Hong Kong by Dai Nippon (H.K.) Ltd.

10 9 8 7 6 5 4 3 2 1

Library of Congress Cataloging-in-Publication Data
Kightley, Rosalinda.
The postman.
Summary: As the postman moves on his rounds through the busy
town, he sees many aspects of its life, from teachers
at the local school to children in the swimming pool.
[1. Postal service—Letter carriers—Fiction.
2. City and town life—Fiction. 3. Stories in rhyme] I. Title.
PZ8.3.K54Po 1988   [E]   87-14160
ISBN 0-02-750270-8

The Postman

Rosalinda Kightley

MACMILLAN PUBLISHING COMPANY
New York

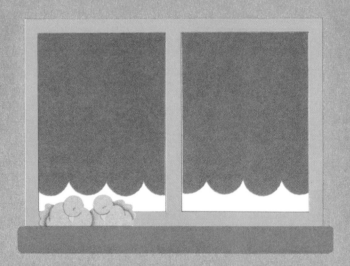

The postman calls at number three,

Now he's at the market. See?

He gets to the station before it's light,

Has a chat with the workers

on the building site.

He brings letters to the teachers

at the local school,

And waves to the children

at the swimming pool.

He has mail for the shops

at the bottom of the hill,

And a package for the lady

with the check-out bill.

There's an airmail letter

JOE AND DAN'S

for Joe and Dan,

A postcard for the man

with the ice-cream van.

At last the postman's bag is empty…

TIP-TOP
TOYS

And home he rides

to number twenty.